4

THERE'S NOTHING LIKE AN EARLY MORNING CHASE TO GET THE OL' HEART A-PUMPING.

AND YOU LOOK LIKE YOU COULD DEFINITELY USE THE EXERCISE.

RUMBLE

I'M ALIVE!

I'M DEAD.

THANKS TO **YOU**, I HAVE NO FOOD.

AND NO FOOD PLUS WINTER EQUALS...

...DEATH.

AN UMBRELLA, A SHOVEL, POTS AND PANS...

...YOU'RE BRINGING EVERYTHING BUT THE KITCHEN SINK.

YOU CAN NEVER BE TOO PREPARED.

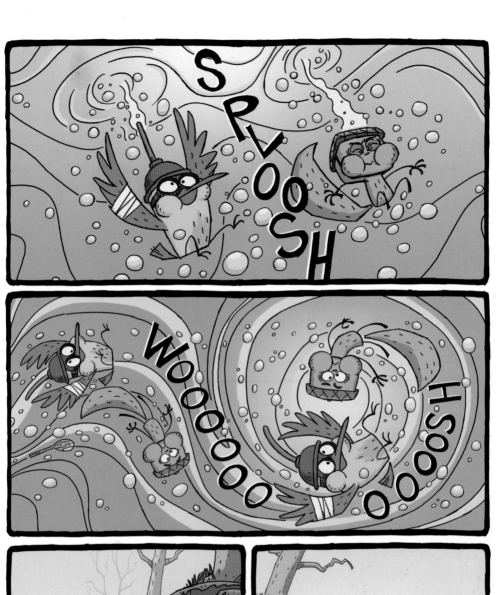

50

55

SNAKES.

SPIDERS.

BATS.

A DEADLY WASP!

WHO WILL PARALYZE US WITH A SINGLE STING, THEN LAY ITS EGGS ON OUR BACKS AND ITS LARVAE WILL HATCH AND FEED ON OUR INSIDES WHILE WE'RE **STILL ALIVE!!**

HEY, LOOK, THERE'S SOMETHING COMING THIS WAY.

I DON'T WANT TO BE WASP FOOD!!!

58

59

60

ONE TIME, I SAW A NUT THE SIZE OF A SMALL BOULDER.

IT TOOK ME THE WHOLE DAY TO GET IT UP MY TREE.

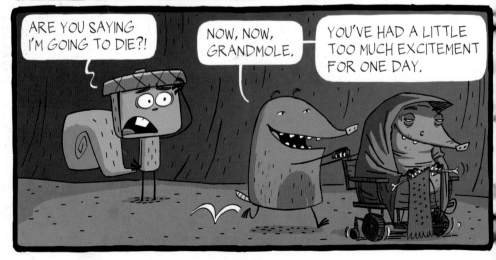

LATER...

YOU BOYS SHOULD BE COMFORTABLE IN HERE.

UH, MRS. MOLE, HAVE ANY OF GRANDMOLE'S PREDICTIONS EVER COME TRUE?

WHEEEEEE!

OH, DON'T BE SILLY.

GRANDMOLE RARELY MAKES ANY SENSE.

CHATTER

YOU'RE NOT GOING TO **BEE**-LIEVE THIS, BUT I'M NOT REALLY A BEE.

OUCH! NOW, NOW, NO NEED TO GET **BEE**-ENT OUT OF SHAPE.

OUCH! OUCH!... **BEE**-HAVE YOURSELF!

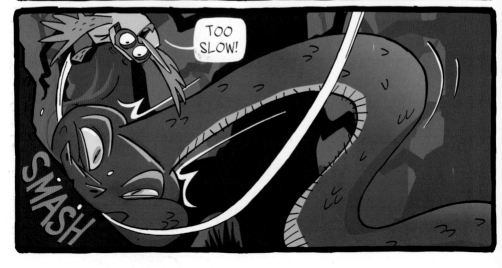

...AND YOU GO WHERE THE WIND TAKES YOU.

YOU WANT ME TO TAKE YOU UP?

NAH, I'M JUST STARTING TO ENJOY MYSELF...

...PROBABLY BEST IF WE PUT OFF MY INEVITABLE DEATH UNTIL LATER.

GOOD POINT.

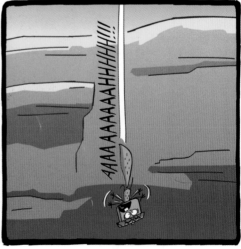

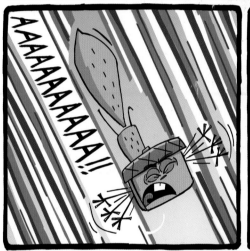

I THINK I'VE MET MY MATCH...

SNAP

...GOTTA GO!

SQUIRREL, ARE YOU OKAY?

SQUIRREL?!

SQUIRREL?

114

OKAY, FINE, I'LL PUT YOU IN OUR THEME SONG...

...BUT YOU'RE GOING TO HAVE TO CLEAN YOURSELF UP FIRST.

AND FRESHEN YOUR BREATH.

THWACK

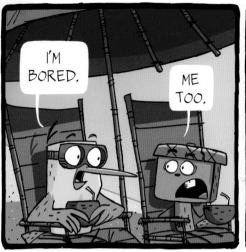

THE END.